THE CARDENDEN COLLECTION

VOLUME ONE

68 original compositions for accordion, fiddle and bagpipes by
MICHAEL PHILIP

Includes a section arranged for the bagpipes

The Michael Philip Scottish Dance Band, circa 1987.
From left to right: Brian Morrison, Davie Bell, Michael Philip, Suzanne Gray,
Alison Dewar, Robert Ross

Published by Deeay Music, Forfar, February 2005

Acknowledgements

I would like to thank the following people for their time, patience and assistance. Without their help, this book would not have been possible:

Graham Berry, for transcribing, arranging chords and typesetting the music;

Paul Clancy, for co-writing several tunes, and arranging harmony parts;

Brian Lamond, Pipe Major of Dysart and Dundonald Pipe Band, for arranging the bagpipe settings;

Marcus Davidson, for typesetting the bagpipe arrangements;

Joan Manuel, for editorial work;

Doug Adamson, for advice regarding publishing the book;

Kaz, for the painting used on the front cover;

Bill Wilkie, MBE, for his kind words in the introduction;

Mabel Gray, for her encouragement over the years.

Music transcribed and typeset by Graham Berry

Front cover artwork from an original painting by Kaz.

Printed by Multiprint, Seafield Road, Kirkcaldy, KY1 1SR

Michael Philip and Paul Clancy
The Whistling Ferryman (CDPM002)

Conundrum Showband
Perfect Day (CDPM004)

www.conundrumshowband.com

CDs available from Michael Philip, 01592 720677 (free estimates for decoration!)

INTRODUCTION

At last, with the publication of this book, we can all play the original and inspired compositions by MICHAEL PHILIP of Cardenden, Fife. Michael has an incredible technique and I'm always amazed that someone who is a Painter and Decorator to trade can have such dexterity on the accordion. For this reason his tunes are technically demanding but absolutely dazzlingly brilliant, always fresh, never monotonous and like all good compositions, built on innovative harmonies. Michael has a gift for this. He has won the Composition Section in the Perth Festival five times which is proof of his great ability.

Studying under the late Joe Burke then with Mary Paterson, both also of Cardenden and both accomplished musicians and master accordionists whose knowledge and playing abilities covered a wide spectrum of music, Michael was pointed in the right direction from the very beginning and received a thorough grounding in music which I am sure has been the foundation of his subsequent success. Michael was also coached for several Festivals by Peter Bruce the renowned teacher of so many Scottish Champions and of course under the tutelage of Peter he won the All Scotland Open Solo Championship in the Year 2000.

Michael's experience in the band business has also contributed to his composing skills. He is Leader of the Conundrum Showband performing and working with Paul Clancy (a virtuoso musician in his own right) for the last 17 years. They have in fact worked together on four of the tunes featured. Paul has also arranged second-part harmonies for a number of the compositions.

You will find the music in this book exciting and refreshing, and like a good novel you will be unable to lay it down. It is quite out of the ordinary and great value. I know you will enjoy it and it gives me tremendous pleasure to write this introduction.

Heartiest congratulations to Michael on this work.

Bill Wilkie, M.B.E.

BEHIND THE MUSIC

People, Events, Occasions, Scenery etc. – all of which have inspired me over the last 20 years to compose the music in this book. I hope you will enjoy playing and listening to this collection.

Michael Philip

Jim Wilson of Cardenden

A personal friend, this March is dedicated to Jim who is a well-known personality in Cardenden for his humour, poetic wit, fishing expertise (he casts a "braw bramble worm") but especially for his superb tenor voice. Jim has performed with me at many charity functions.

The Lady Helen's Jig, The Checkweighman, The Rope Splicer and The Snibbler

Four tunes written for a Mining Album. Lady Helen is the name of one of the local Collieries and the other 3 tunes relate to jobs in the pits. The Lady Helen's Jig was also adopted by the RSCDS as the original tune for the dance "Hall Change" in Book 42 (Scottish Country Dances to celebrate the 70th Summer School held in St Andrews).

Bill Wilkie's 51st Festival March

Bill needs no introduction in the Scottish music scene. A stalwart of the Scottish Championships for over 55 years, he is a worthy recipient of the M.B.E. for his contribution to music and teaching and this is my small tribute to him. The tune sits proudly framed in his shop in Perth.

The City of Newcastle Pipe Band

This tune was written for the 75th anniversary of the band while I was in Gateshead a number of years ago working for the Scottish Tourist Board. The tune was framed and presented to the Band by Charles Currie (son of the late Reverend James Currie of Arran), representing the Scottish Tourist Board.

Miss Susan MacFadyen

I composed this March for Susan at the Shetland Accordion and Fiddle Festival in October 2004. Susan is a very talented accordionist who loves to play pipe music and has won numerous competitions in this field, in particular first place in the Pipe Music section at the Perth Festival in 2004. I wish her all the success in the future.

Ella

A Waltz dedicated to the late Ella Scott of Lochgelly, who was a talented accordionist from the "old school". Ella was not only in great demand for her playing abilities at local functions, but was also a member of a local group of entertainers called "Us Girls".

The Reverend E R Campbell of Auchterderran and The Auld Kirk

Two Marches written for the Rev. Campbell to commemorate his 25 years in the Cardenden community at Auchterderran & St Fothad's Parish Church.

The Den Burn Reel

Flowing through Cardenden, I have many "wet" memories trying to jump over the burn in my "young days". The first two parts of this tune are in RSCDS Book 43 and comprise the original tune for the dance "Bea's Delight". The third and fourth parts were written as a competition piece. It's an unusual tune in the key of C minor with a "tricky" ending.

The Whistling Ferryman

Written for Nigel the Ferryman from Craignure on the Isle of Mull. This is the title track of an album recorded with Paul Clancy. The tune captures the mystical sea over the Sound of Mull.

The Links Reel, The Rib Tickler, The Helter Skelter and The Carousel Gallopers

All four tunes were composed to commemorate the 700 years of Kirkcaldy Links Market in April 2004. They form part of the CD of music "Market Nights" produced by my band Conundrum for the 700 years Anniversary depicting the style of the Market from its beginnings to present times.

Keir's Brae

A March written for the famous Pipe Major R T Shepherd, M.B.E. "Keir's Brae" is the street where Bobby has lived for a number of years. I first encountered Bobby when I was 4 years old when my mother was keen for me to play drums with Dysart & Dundonald Pipe Band.

Mary Paterson of Annfield House

Mary was one of my tutors in my early years. This Reel is dedicated to Mary for her patience and invaluable contribution to my playing abilities and was written in Mary's music room at Annfield House.

Mary McCormack

The late Mary McCormack is the sister of John McCormack, Drummer in the Conundrum Showband. Mary was the heart and soul of every party and this Reel was written in Shetland along with Paul Clancy. The reel is dedicated to Mary.

Davie Bell the Greenkeeper

Davie is not just an excellent Scottish Dance Band Drummer, you should try the greens at Rosemount Golf Club, Blairgowrie.

Nancy Barrowman's Fancy

Written for local man Boswell Allan. However I preferred to name the tune after Boswell's wife Nancy Barrowman.

The View from Glenniston

Whilst decorating the lounge at Glenniston Farm, I was inspired to compose this slow air by the picturesque view looking towards Cardenden. This tune is currently being played by Dysart & Dundonald Pipe Band and is to be recorded on their latest album.

The Lady Josephine March

Again for the Mining Project, The Lady Josephine is the name of the once prominent Bowhill Colliery in Cardenden, Fife.

Tribute to Charles Kennedy

A Past President of the World Burns Federation, local man Charles Kennedy also held Country Dance classes with numbers exceeding 400 in Bowhill and Cardenden in the early 60s. Charles is a personal friend who still to this day takes a great interest in my music.

Mary & Hubert Hurst's Waltz

Composed for Mary & Hubert Hurst (of St Helens, Lancashire) as part of the surprise celebrations for their Golden Wedding Anniversary in July 2004 in Cardenden, and as a tribute to Hubert's love of Scotland and Scottish Accordion music. Mary is a "Scottish lass" originally from Lochgelly.

John McConnell's No. 9

John has a great personality and performed with me in the Colm Cille Ceilidh Band in my early years. He is a great enthusiast of traditional Irish music and helps me to find unusual pieces for various recordings and functions.

Willie Dowds of Burt

Bill appeared at my door and asked me to join the Colm Cille Ceilidh Band (at a point when, aged 18 at the time, I had practically given up playing altogether). You can safely say if it wasn't for now the late Bill Dowds of Burt, my successes and the publication of this book might never have transpired, so it gives me the greatest pleasure to include this tune.

Nicol Iain McLaren

Nicol needs no introduction to the Scottish music scene as not only is he Chairman of the NAAFC but a great band leader in his own right. This tune was written as a "thank you" to Nicol for all his encouragement and help to me in forming the new "Michael Philip Scottish Dance Band".

Bob McMath's Birthday Polka

A technical wizard with the accordion, this Polka was written for Bob on his birthday as a tribute for all the help and encouragement he gives me.

Cameron McArthur

Cameron lives next door to me and plays bagpipes in Lochgelly High School Pipe Band. I wish young Cameron all the success with his piping career.

Annfield House Jig

On the outskirts of Cardenden, Annfield House is the home of Mary Paterson.

Lynn Tucker's Reel

Lynn is a brilliant traditional folk music accordionist from Rothbury, Northumberland, who played alongside me for the first time at Auchtermuchty Festival in 2003 and this composition is a small tribute to her.

Meisner's Waistcoat

Glen Meisner, Musical Director of various Scottish Shows in which I have performed, particularly in Edinburgh - you don't need to go far over the Bridge from Fife to see Glen's famous waistcoat, hence the name!

The Busker's Nightmare

Written along with Paul Clancy whilst at one of the Shetland Festivals, this tune is not just a nightmare for Buskers – give it a try!

Derek's Wonky Keyboard

Derek Hendry now stays in Shetland but before he moved there from the Angus area the Band borrowed his keyboard to play at the Oban Accordion & Fiddle Club, with drastic consequences!!

Ishbel's Reel

Ishbel is the mother of the past Scottish Champion Robert Ross, originally from Kincardine, Fife. Sadly Ishbel died from Motor Neurone disease but this tune typifies her personality and as a valued friend she is very much missed by all my family.

Elizabeth McConnell

Liz, who hails from Newcastle, has a lovely folk voice and is a brilliant folk guitarist. She worked with me at the Metro Centre in Gateshead for the Scottish Tourist Board in September 2004 and I hope to work with her again in the near future. This reel is a small tribute to Liz and her personality.

Willie Robertson

A great fiddle player, Willie has a gift for playing slow airs. Originally from Cardenden, he is a stalwart of the Fife Strathspey and Reel Society. This tune is Willie to a tee!

The March, Morag Robertson

Morag, a first class musician and teacher, also has the shop Music Corner in Laurieston, near Falkirk. She has 2 very talented sons in the band scene, Gordon & Findlay. Gordon recorded with me on my "Live at the Riverside" album. This tune was written for Morag as a thank you for her help and sound advice in supplying the "perfect accordion".

Oban Festival March

My first composition written 20 years ago which took 1st place at the All Scotland Perth Festival in 1985 and also 1st at Musselburgh Festival in the "Own Composition" Section. Unfortunately the tune didn't get placed at Oban Festival - the Adjudicator said it should have been first for the name!

Willie Johnstone of Dunnydeer

Willie of Dunnydeer, Aberdeenshire, and who now lives in Perth, is Fiddle player in my Scottish Dance Band. This tune was written for Willie as a thank you for all the hard work he puts into the band.

Kyle of Dunkirk

The late George Kyle was a man of many talents - not just a first class comedian and entertainer, he was also a professional Goalkeeper and a Sergeant Major in the Army. In show business George worked with all the top Scottish stars. George was Chairman of the Scottish Branch of the Dunkirk Veterans' Association - hence the title.

Leavin' the Fair

Written along with Paul Clancy, this is the last track on the "Market Nights" album commemorating 700 years of Kirkcaldy Links Market.

The Meteorite, The Octopus and The Steamboat Jig

Again written for the 700 years Links Market Album, these 3 Jigs are named after popular fairground rides.

Jean of West Baila

Jean is from Lerwick, Shetland, and Paul Clancy and I have stayed at her home during many Shetland festivals. This tune was one of the pieces composed with Paul in Jean's living room. This slow air is a thank you for her very kind hospitality - and by the way, Jean maks a great "pat" of salt mutton soup!

Bryce Johnston's Jig

Bryce is an excellent harmonica player and this tune was written as a tribute to the "master of the moothie".

Peter Bruce, the Tutor

From Scone, Perthshire, Peter has to be one of if not the top accordion teachers in Scotland. I remember my first lesson when I asked him for the music to the March Harry Scott of Friockheim. So as I was playing the March Willie Atkinson, Peter wrote out Harry Scott with the right hand, left hand and fingering without even picking up an accordion - to me that's a genius. I would like to take this opportunity to say a very grateful "Thank you for your patience, time and encouragement over the years".

A Waltz for Issy

Issy Hodgson from Prestonpans loves traditional music. A first class pianist, Issy deputised with the band at very short notice and did a grand job. No doubt we will have the pleasure of playing together again in the near future.

Kirsty Megan's Reel and Jig

Two tunes written for my daughter Kirsty when she was a toddler. Now nearly 14, Kirsty is a lovely girl and makes me very proud - even though she stopped her piano lessons.

Dr Martha George

This march was written as a retirement present. I was asked to write the tune by friends of the doctor and the band played the March as a tribute to her at the retiral party in Broughty Ferry.

Mrs Carol Clancy

This strathspey was written for Carol, wife of Paul, and recorded on Conundrum's "Crossing the Border" album. This is an unusual tune that can be played for competition or dance.

Farewell to Longannet

Longannet Mine was the last pit in Fife to be shut down. Again written for the Mining Project it was also adopted by the RSCDS and is included in Book 43 (the Jubilee Collection).

Master Daniel Philip

Now 9 years old, my eldest son Daniel is a very musical boy. This reel, along with the strathspey Nancy Barrowman's Fancy, was part of the selection which won me the Scottish Senior Accordion Championship at Perth in October 2000.

Colin Coull of Buckie

Colin, from Buckie, latterly stayed in Blairgowrie and was famous for his colourful kilts. This tune was composed for the Country Dance "Colin's Kilts". Sadly Colin passed away in 2002.

Glenrothes 50th Anniversary March

As part of the celebrations for 50 years of Glenrothes town, Brand-Rex, one of the major employers in the town, sponsored a competition at the Rothes Hall. This was to write a tune to commemorate the anniversary. I entered this tune and after the panel took some considerable time to deliberate the winner, my Pipe March came up trumps and won the title.

Miss Suzanne Gray

Originally from Clackmannan, Suzanne is a wonderful bass player and a very talented lady. The Gray family has been prominent in the traditional music scene for as long as I can remember and I have had the pleasure of working with Suzanne for over 20 years. Suzanne complained about the tune saying no one could play it - but that's not the case!

Anita McKain of Freuchie

Daughter of the famous pipe music accordionist and adjudicator John Crawford, Anita was taught by Bill Wilkie and is a very talented accordionist in her own right. I am told that Anita is a bit shy to perform on stage – a bit like myself!!! Anita has recently recorded on her father's new CD.

The Diamond Wedding Waltz

Written for Peter and Agnes Dewar of Cardenden, who are my friend Jim Wilson's in-laws. This tune was composed to commemorate their Diamond Wedding held in Bowhill Club on the 31st of March 2000.

A Tribute to Jim Thom of Guildtown

The late Jim Thom was a great help to my eventual success in winning both Musselburgh and Perth Festivals. He advised me to play more of a traditional nature rather than technical tunes. He said "I don't know about the judges but if I was in the audience I would rather listen to the more traditional style and I'm sure the rest of the audience would agree". It did the trick! I would like to wish his family all the very best.

Index

Standard Settings

Bagpipe Settings

Jim Wilson of Cardenden

March

Michael Philip

1

The Lady Helen's Jig

Jig

Michael Philip

The Checkweighman

Jig

Michael Philip

The Rope Splicer

Jig

Michael Philip

The Snibbler

Jig

Michael Philip

3

Bill Wilkie's 51ˢᵗ Festival March

March

Michael Philip

4

The City of Newcastle Pipe Band

March

Michael Philip

5

Miss Susan MacFadyen

March

Michael Philip

Ella

Waltz

Michael Philip

Reverend E R Campbell of Auchterderran

Grand March

Michael Philip

The Auld Kirk

Grand March

Michael Philip

9

The Den Burn

Reel

Michael Philip

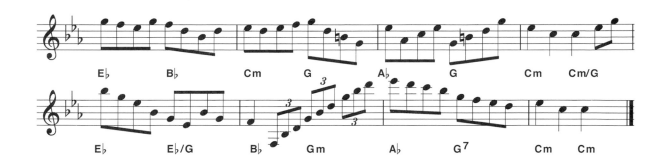

The Whistling Ferryman

Slow Air

Michael Philip

Fine

D.C. al Fine

The Links Reel

Reel

Michael Philip

The Rib Tickler

Reel

Michael Philip

The Helter Skelter

Reel

Michael Philip

The Carousel Gallopers

Jig

Michael Philip

13

Keir's Brae

March

Michael Philip

Mary Paterson of Annfield House

Reel

Michael Philip

Mary McCormack

Reel

Michael Philip and Paul Clancy

Davie Bell the Greenkeeper

Two-Step

Michael Philip

Nancy Barrowman's Fancy

Strathspey

Michael Philip

The View from Glenniston

Slow Air

Michael Philip

The Lady Josephine March

March

Michael Philip

19

Tribute to Charles Kennedy

Reel

Michael Philip

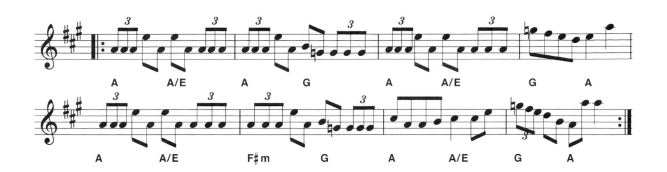

Mary and Hubert Hurst's Waltz

Waltz

Michael Philip

John McConnell's No. 9

Jig

Michael Philip

Willie Dowds of Burt

Jig

Michael Philip

Nicol Iain McLaren

March

Michael Philip

Bob McMath's Birthday Polka

Polka

Michael Philip

Cameron McArthur

Jig

Michael Philip

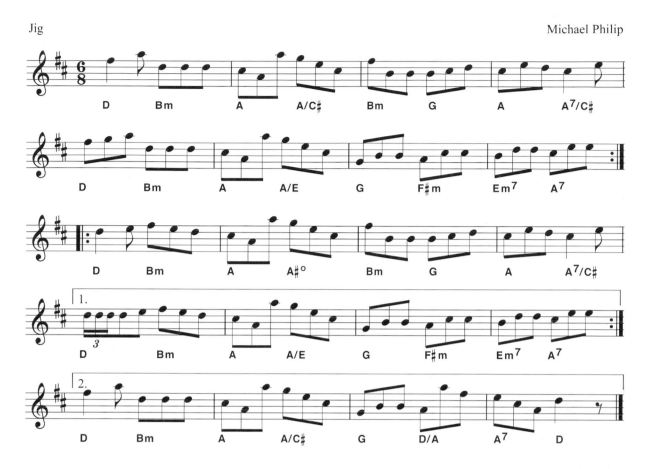

Annfield House Jig

Jig

Michael Philip

Lynn Tucker's Reel

Reel

Michael Philip

Meisner's Waistcoat

Reel

Michael Philip

The Busker's Nightmare

Reel

Michael Philip and Paul Clancy

Derek's Wonky Keyboard

Reel

Michael Philip

Ishbell's Reel

Michael Philip

Reel

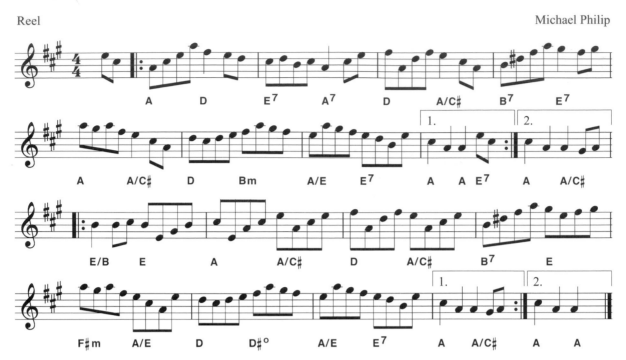

Elizabeth McConnell

Michael Philip

Reel

The March, Morag Robertson

March

Michael Philip

Willie Robertson

Slow Air

Michael Philip

Oban Festival March

March

Michael Philip

31

Willie Johnstone of Dunnydeer

March

Michael Philip

Kyle of Dunkirk

March

Michael Philip

Leavin' the Fair

Slow Air

Michael Philip and Paul Clancy

33

The Meteorite

Jig

Michael Philip

The Octopus

Jig

Michael Philip

Jean of West Baila

Slow Air

Michael Philip & Paul Clancy

35

Bryce Johnston's Jig

Jig

Michael Philip

Peter Bruce, the Tutor

Jig

Michael Philip

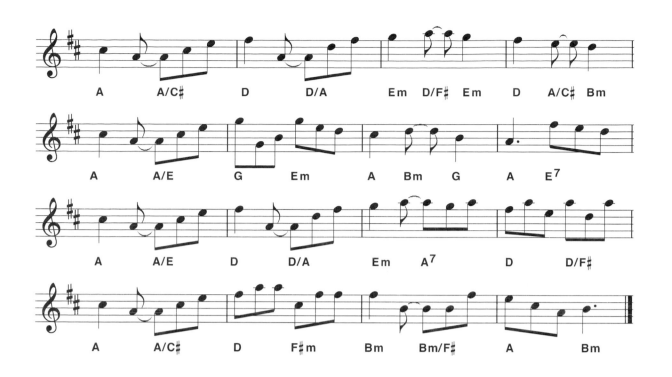

A Waltz for Issy

Waltz

Michael Philip

Kirsty Megan's Reel

Reel

Michael Philip

Kirsty Megan's Jig

Jig

Michael Philip

39

Dr Martha George

March

Michael Philip

Mrs Carol Clancy

Strathspey

Michael Philip

Farewell to Longannet

Slow Air

Michael Philip

41

The Steamboat Jig

Jig

Michael Philip

Master Daniel Philip

Reel

Michael Philip

Colin Coull of Buckie

Jig

Michael Philip

Glenrothes 50th Anniversary March

March   Michael Philip

Miss Suzanne Gray

March

Michael Philip

45

Anita McKain of Freuchie

Reel

Michael Philip

The Diamond Wedding Waltz

Waltz

Michael Philip

47

A Tribute to Jim Thom of Guildtown

March

Michael Philip

Settings arranged for the Highland Bagpipe

Keir's Brae

March

Michael Philip

49

Kirsty Megan's Reel

Reel

Michael Philip

Kirsty Megan's Jig

Jig

Michael Philip

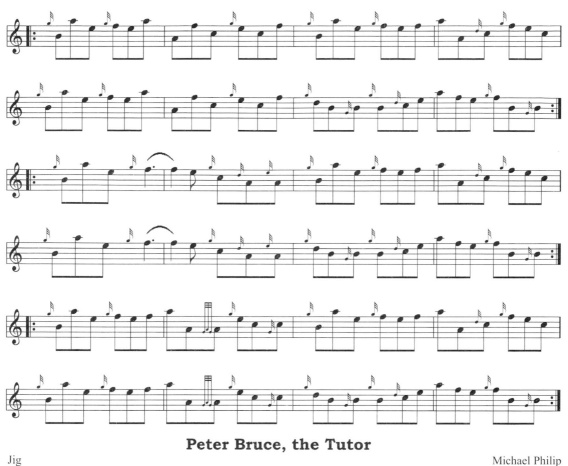

Peter Bruce, the Tutor

Jig

Michael Philip

Bryce Johnston's Jig

Jig

Michael Philip

The View from Glenniston

Slow Air

Michael Philip

Nicol Iain McLaren

March

Michael Philip

53

Anita McKain of Freuchie

Reel

Michael Philip

Glenrothes 50th Anniversary March

March

Michael Philip

Cameron McArthur

Jig

Michael Philip

The City of Newcastle Pipe Band

March

Michael Philip

Miss Susan MacFadyen

March

Michael Philip

Kyle of Dunkirk

March

Michael Philip

Tribute to Charles Kennedy

Reel

Michael Philip